D1500456

mafalda

& friends

QUINO

6

EDICIONES DE LA FLOR

Quino
Mafalda and friends 6. -1ª. ed.- Buenos Aires: Ediciones de la Flor, 2008.
96 p. ; 20x14 cm.

ISBN 978-950-515-786-0

1. Humor gráfico argentino - I. Título
CDD A867

FOR TITO F.

QUINO

WHAT IS PHILOSOPHY, PAPA?

I ASKED MY FATHER TO EXPLAIN THE MEANING OF PHILOSOPHY

AND?

HMM??

I SEE

"KILLS FLIES, MOSQUITOES, MIDGES, SPIDERS, WASPS, COCKROACHES AND OTHER INSECTS IN THE HOME"

"HOW TO USE: AIM THE SPOUT OF THE SPRAY AT THE INSECT TO BE KILLED SPRAYING FROM A DISTANCE OF 30 CM"

FFFFFFT!

PLEASE NOTE PEOPLE USUALLY GET KILLED WITH LESS LITERATURE

903

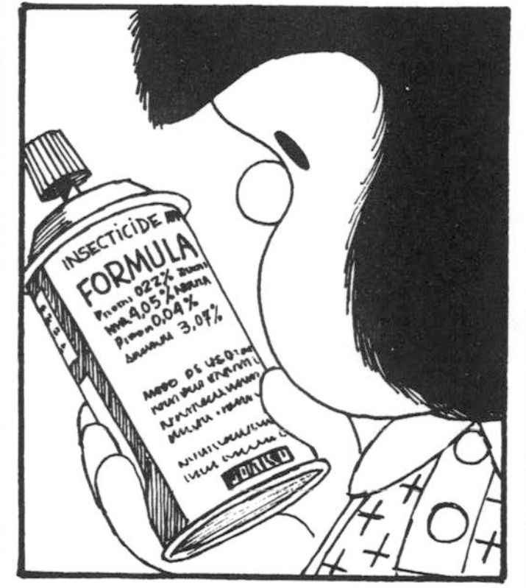
INSECTICIDE
FORMULA

BEAR ME NO GRUDGE, THE PIPPONILE DIOXIDE IS TO BLAME

LADIES, GET A "WASHEX" THE NEW AUTOMATIC MACHINE!

SO SIMPLE EVEN A CHILD CAN USE IT!

AND YOU HAVE TO USE US TO SHOW THAT EVEN INCOMPETENT WOMEN CAN WORK IT?

SAY, WHEN YOUR BABY BROTHER ARRIVES, WILL YOU STILL LIKE ME?

MIGUELITO...! HOW CAN YOU SAY SUCH A THING? OF COURSE I WILL LIKE YOU AS ALWAYS

AHH!

THUMP!

MIGUELITO IS AFRAID THAT I WILL LIKE HIM LESS WHEN MY BABY BROTHER ARRIVES
OH?

IN FACT I AM A LITTLE SCARED THAT YOU WILL LOVE ME LESS WHEN HE ARRIVES

SILLY! I WILL NEVER STOP LOVING YOU NOT ONE LITTLE BIT

I KNOW, BUT IT'S AS IF YOUR LOVE HAD OPENED A BRANCH OFFICE

DON MANOLO...THE PRICE OF THIS CAN OF BEANS IS ARMED ROBBERY!

WE HAVE ANOTHER, CHEAPER BRAND, MADAM

TCH! WHO KNOWS WHY THEY ARE CHEAPER! YOU HAVE TO BE SO CAREFUL! SO, WELL, LOOK...

...BETTER GIVE ME THE EXPENSIVE ONE. IT'S ROBBERY, BUT, WE'RE ACCUSTOMED TO THAT, EH? HA, HA! MY GOODNESS!

WHERE'VE YOU BEEN, MAFALDA?
THE COMEDY THEATRE

...BETTER A REDHEAD, MY COUSINS WILL DIE WITH ENVY WHEN THEY SEE ME WITH SUCH A UNIQUE HUSBAND

IT'S NO USE. NOBODY SPONTANEOUSLY NOTICES THAT I AM A GREAT GUY

WHAT DO YOU THINK I SHOULD DO SO PEOPLE NOTICE THAT ONE IS A GREAT GUY?

LOOK, MIGUELITO: WHAT YOU NEED TO DO IS JUST **THINK** YOU'RE A GREAT GUY

...BECAUSE IF **THEY REALIZE YOU ARE,** YOU'RE DEAD

HELLO. DO YOU HAVE A MAGAZINE WITH PICTURES OF ANIMALS?
PICTURES OF ANIMALS? NNNO...NO

CARETAKER MURDERED
VIOLENCE ON THE FIELD
ROUND
RIOTS ON

LIAR!

IT'LL BE CHRISTMAS IN A MONTH!
LOVELY!

WE CAN START BUILDING THE MANGER WITH THE THREE KINGS AND SANTA CLAUS BRINGING GIFTS!

REALLY!?...SANTA CLAUS DID NOT TAKE GIFTS TO THE MANGER
YOU DON'T SAY

SO THE FAT GUY WAS A TIGHT FIST! LOOK AT THAT!...

OKEY!

CAMMON!

SHARRAP!

WASHANDWEAR!

SOME CABINET CRISIS!

THERE IS NO NEED FOR A DEEP STUDY TO SEE THAT FROM THE BOW AND ARROW!...

...TO INTERCONTINENTAL MISSILES IT IS REMARKANBLE TO SEE HOW MUCH TECHNOLOGY HAS EVOLVED

AND DEPRESSING TO FIND HOW LITTLE INTENTIONS HAVE CHANGED

FOR YOU, MRS SUSANITA
OH!

MY FIRST CHILD! HOW EXCITING!

GOOD MORNING. I'VE COME TO PLAY WITH SUSANITA
SORRY, SHE WOKE UP FEELING SICK AND UNABLE TO GET OUT OF BED

AT LAST! SCHOOL'S OVER!

NO MORE WORRY ABOUT STUDYING AND GETTING HOMEWORK DONE!

AND NOW WHAT WILL WE DO WITH SO MUCH FREEDOM AHEAD?

WHERE ARE WE GOING ON VACATION THIS SUMMER, MAMA?

NOWHERE, MAFALDA; WE HAVE TO STAY HOME AND WAIT FOR YOUR BABY BROTHER TO ARRIVE

COULDN'T THAT HIJACKER HAVE CHOSEN A BETTER TIME?

SNIFF!...
WHAT'S WRONG WITH HER?

NOTHING, SHE JUST LEARNED THAT THIS SUMMER WE CAN'T GO ON VACATION BECAUSE WE HAVE TO WAIT FOR HER BABY BROTHER

YOU MUST UNDERSTAND, MAFALDA. WE JUST CAN'T GO AWAY AND HAVE HIM ARRIVE WHEN WE'RE NOT HERE
WHY NOT?

WE COULD LEAVE THE FRIDGE PACKED FULL OF BOTTLES

920

WHAT'S UP, MAFALDA
MY PARENTS WON'T TAKE ME ON VACATION THIS SUMMER BECAUSE WE HAVE TO WAIT FOR MY BABY BROTHER

SORRY, IT WAS A FACIAL SLIP

I'M SORRY FOR MAFALDA. SHE TOLD ME THAT THIS SUMMER SHE **CAN'T** GO ON VACATION WITH HER PARENTS
WHY NOT?

BECAUSE THEY HAVE TO WAIT FOR HER BABY BROTHER
OF COURSE

YOU CAN'T IMAGINE HOW SORRY I FELT TO SEE HER SO SAD. LOOK, POOR THING! THERE SHE IS

HELLO, MAFALDA
HI, HOW'RE YOU?

OH...! FAB, BECAUSE NOW WE CAN START TO THINK OF HOLIDAYS!

HULLO!
HULLO!

DO YOU KNOW ABOUT THE DELICIOUS CHOCOLATES, CHRISTMAS CAKES AND NUTS OFFERED AT MANOLITO'S STORE WONDERFUL!
WHEN DID YOU TRY ALL THOSE THINGS, MANOLITO?

NEVER, BUT HE **PAYS ME** WITH SWEETS

DEPARMENT OF INLAND REVENUE

AND THE WORST OF IT IS THE FEELING OF LEMON JUICE RUNNING IN MY VEINS

I SAW A PHOTO OF THE EARTH TAKEN FROM A SATELLITE

IT MUST HAVE BEEN A BLACK BLOB BECAUSE THOSE SATELLITES COME OVER AT NIGHT, RIGHT?

NO. THE THING IS WE SEE THEM AT NIGHT AND BY DAY WE DON'T. BUT THEY PASS AT ANY TIME

DO YOU HAVE A HAIR BRUSH TO LEND ME?

Cider and Christmas cake
at "Don Manolo" store
Try them and see!

!
istmas cake
olo" store
nd see!

MEDICAL DOCTOR
1197
Cider and Christmas cake
at "Don Manolo" store
Try them and see!
WHAT A PSYCHOLOGICAL DISASTER!

YESTERDAY I READ THAT IF WE ALL TRIED SOMETHING THE WORLD WOULD BE A BETTER PLACE:

"DO GOOD AND LET IT NOT MATTER TO WHOM"

MMMMMHHH!

...I THINK THE BEST ABOUT STARTING A NEW YEAR IS THAT WE GET CLOSER TO REACHING THE FUTURE

HULLO, I'M NEW IN TOWN

AND THE FIRST THING THAT CAUGHT MY EYE IS THE "DON MANOLO" STORE. WHAT GOOD PRICES! AND ALSO...

...EVERYTHING THEY SELL IS FIRST CLA...

EXCEPT THE HAIR OIL!

"THE CHART ILLUSTRATES THE COMPARATIVE FIRE POWER OF RUSSIA, CHINA AND THE USA"

For the Judge

FELIPE, WOULD YOU GO AND BUY MILK?

SORRY, MAMA, I DON'T HAVE TIME

FUNNY, ADULTS BELIEVE THAT LIE WHEN THEY SAY IT

MBSSNSSBNS NSSSTRBLSS? EEHEE?

MMMH!...MNSBLTS BSSLZZMBSSNS!

WELL?

14

15
BRiip

15
DECEMBER

THIS GUY JUST EATS UP TIME
AND IS SKINNIER EVERY DAY
15

MAGAZINES

HEY! **WHO** DOES
THIS LOOK LIKE?

NANCY

MY GRANNY?
NANCY

LESS THAN A MONTH TO GO FOR THE THREE KINGS' DAY, RIGHT, MAMA?
THAT'S RIGHT

THEY COME FROM THE MIDDLE EAST, **DON'T THEY?**
YEEES, OF COURSE

TCH! I WONDER IF THEY ARE ARABS OR ISRAELIS?
THEY HAVE ALWAYS REMAINED ABOVE POLITICAL ISSUES, DEAR

HOW VERY CONVENIENT THAT THEY ARE KINGS SO AS NOT TO EXPLAIN ANYTHING, EH?

GEORGIA (AFP) –A SKELETON FOUND HERE HAS LED RUSSIAN SCIENTISTS TO CONFIRM THAT THE OSTRICHES OF FIVE MILLION YEARS AGO WERE TWICE AS LARGE AS THOSE TODAY
AHA!

THAT'S THE REASON! I ALWAYS WONDERED HOW THE CAVELADIES MANAGED WITH THE CLEANING IN THOSE GREAT PREHISTORIC CAVES

BUT, IT'S EASY, THEIR FEATHER DUSTERS WERE MUCH LARGER THAN THOSE WE HAVE NOW!

"fashionable"
lentils?
Don Manolo
Store
BOUNCE!

I'M OFF TO THE DRY CLEANERS. LOOK AFTER YOUR BROTHER FOR A MINUTE. I'LL BE BACK IMMEDIATELY, OK?
OK

SLUPP!

WAAAH!...
OH, OK! HAVE IT!

IF THE PEOPLE OF THE WORLD USED LUNGS LIKE THAT, DICTATORS WOULD STAND NO CHANCE

'COURSE, AGED TWO MONTHS AND IN A CRIB, YOU HAVEN'T THE SLIGHTEST IDEA OF WHAT HAPPENS IN THE WORLD

CRUCH CRUCH
RIGHT?

OBVIOUSLY **NOT**

HOW DID YOUR BROTHER BEHAVE?
FINE

I THOUGHT I'D TAKE AWAY HIS PACIFIER AND HE HOWLED
OH, VERY NICE

YOU SHOULD BE ASHAMED! A BIG GIRL MAKING A TINY BOY SUFFER! WHERE'VE YOU EVER SEEN THAT?

AT THE UN?

MY MUM JUST SCOLDED ME FOR TAKING THE PACIFIER FROM MY BROTHER AND MAKING HIM CRY

I CAN'T SEE WHY HE'S SO KEEN ON A PACIFIER, AFTER ALL

HE SPENDS THE WHOLE DAY SUCKING, TO GET **WHAT? NOTHING!** AND YET HE STILL SUCKS

I THINK HE'S QUITE RIGHT. AT HIS AGE I ALSO EXPECTED SOMETHING OUT OF LIFE

WE LOVE THE PEOPLE, THAT'S WHY WE THINK IT'S WRONG...

...TO PUMP THEM FULL OF BULLETS OR FRY THEM WITH BOMBS

WE DON'T KNOW WHO'S TO BLAME, BUT SO MUCH VIOLENCE IS GETTING ON OUR NERVES

THAT WAS THE PROTEST SONG: *"THE GOOD GUYS ARE GETTING TIRED"*

SAY, MANOLITO, DO YOU THINK PROTEST SONGS WILL MAKE A CHANGE IN THE WORLD?

OF COURSE, A WOMAN CAME TO MY FATHER'S STORE YESTERDAY AND LET HIM HAVE A CONVINCING PROTEST BALLAD: "THE BEANS ARE VERY EXPENSIVE!"

MY FATHER WAS MOVED AND CUT THE PRICE OF BEANS AND OF ALL THE OTHER GOODS

REMARKABLE HOW THIS GIRL PICKS UP SUBTLETY

MAYBE THE PROTEST SONGS ARE USELESS

MANOLITO THINKS NOBODY GETS ANYWHERE BY YELLING WITH A GUITAR AND HE MAY BE RIGHT

WAAAH! WAAAH!

WAAAH!

MAYBE THE GUITAR IS NOT ESSENTIAL

SGLUB
SGLUB

SGLUB
SGLUB
SGLUB

SGLUB
SGLUB
SGLUB
SGLUB

HE PROBABLY THINKS YOU'RE VENEZUELA AND HE IS THE SOMETHING OIL COMPANY?
SGLUB
SGLUB

MAMA, I AM GOING TO THE SQUARE WITH THE KIDS TO PLAY COWBOY!
OK, BE CAREFUL, EH?

MAFALDA IS SUCH A...! SHE'S JUST AS SOON FOR GOODNESS AND PEACE AND ALL THAT...
SUPPORT LTNS
LOVE THY NEIGHBOUR SOCIETY

...AS FOR PLAYING AT VIOLENCE, GUNFIGHTS AND ALL THAT
WE NOW CONTINUE WITH COMMANDO 217
COMMANDO 217

REALLY, CHILDREN TODAY ARE SO HARD TO UNDERSTAND
RATAT-TATATATAT-TATAT-

OK, LET'S PLAY WE HAVE TWO GANGS: THE GOOD GUYS AND THE BAD, EH?

I AM WITH THE GOOD GANG!

C'MON! WE WON'T GET ANYWHERE IF WE'RE ALL GOOD

BANG!
YOU'RE DONE, MIGUELITO
NO, NO! BANG!

I SHOT FIRST. WHY PLAY IF YOU DON'T WANT TO DIE WHEN YOU'RE KILLED?

'CAUSE I READ THAT KIDS NEED TO PLAY KILLING OTHERS TO UNLOAD THE ANGER WE CARRY INSIDE AND ALL THAT

SO IF YOU'RE GOING TO SPOIL MY THERAPY SO SOON, I'M NOT PLAYING

OK! ALL THAT STUFF ABOUT POVERTY, RACISM AND WAR STOPS HERE!

SUSANITA! WE'RE PLAYING OLD FASHIONED COWBOYS! THE OLD FASHIONED ONES!

PTUG!

BLUP!

SEEMS THIS GENERATION COMES WELL PROFILED

"KILLS IN-LAW IN ARGUMENT"

"MOTHER POISONS TWO SMALL CHILDREN"

"GRANNY'S KILLER CONFESSES"

KNOW SOMETHING...? I'VE BEEN READING ABOUT HOW GOOD I AM

WHEN I READ THE CRIME PAGES AND SEE THE HORRORS COMMITTED BY OTHERS...YOU SHOULD SEE HOW GOOD I FEEL

WRONG, SUSANITA. YOU SOULD NEVER COMPARE YOURSELF TO THOSE WORSE THAN YOU, ONLY WITH THOSE WHO ARE BETTER

C'MON! WHO WOULD DO SOMETHING SO AWFUL TOO THEIR OWN PERSONALITY?

SOMETIMES SUSANITA SAYS SUCH STRANGE THINGS!
WHY? WHAT'S SHE SAID NOW?

THAT WHEN SHE READS THE CRIME PAGES AND SEES THE HORRORS COMMITTED BY OTHERS SHE FEELS REALLY GOOD

ONLY A FOOL COULD THINK OF SOMETHING SO STUPID...

WHAT DOES PROFILE MEAN, MAFALDA? WHEN IS IT USED?

PROFILE, MANOLITO, IS USED WHEN SOMETHING IS SEEN TO BE FINE, OR NOT SO CLEAR. A PERSON CAN HAVE A HIGH OR A LOW PROFILE, UNDERSTAND?

GROCERIES
DON MANOLO

UNDERSTOOD

YOU SOULD SEE THE WOMEN WHEN THEY COMPLAIN ABOUT SOMETHING THEY BOUGHT!
YES, BUT YOU SHOULDN'T HIDE FROM ANYTHING

YES, YES! HIDE, MANOLITO! YOU MUST HIDE!
WHY, WHAT'S HAPPENED?

I HEARD THE RADIO SAY THERE IS FREEDOM OF THOUGHT! FREEDOM OF THOUGHT IN THE COUNTRY!

YOU HAVEN'T GOT ONE!
WHO KNOWS WHAT'LL HAPPEN TO YOU!?

OUT!

HEY! HEY! YOU COULD BE MORE GENTLE! FLIES AREN'T SO BAD AFTER ALL!
NOT THEM

BUT ON EACH FLIGHT THEY CARRY GERMS EVERYWHERE!
REALLY?

SO FLIES ARE SOMETHING LIKE AN AMERICAN AIRLINES OF GERMS!? LOOK AT THAT!

I THOUGHT OF A GREAT JOKE AND DREW IT

BREAK GLASS IN CASE OF WAR

I DON'T UNDERSTAND... WHY THE SPOON?
TO COLLECT WHAT'S LEFT OF HUMANITY! ISN'T THAT FUNNY?

WHAT'S HAPPENED TO PEOPLE'S SENSE OF HUMOUR

I HAVE NOTICED THAT I AM REFINED, AGREEABLE AND PLEASANT

THAT IS NOT FALSE MODESTY, NO

THANKS TO MY HUMBLE HONESTY I DISCOVERED HOW I AM REALLY

NOBODY IS A GOOD SHERLOCK HOLMES OF ONESELF

HEE-HEE-
HEE!

HEE-
HEE-
HEE!
?

WHAT'S UP WITH GUILLE, PAPA? WHY IS HE LAUGHING
HEE-
HEE-
HEE!

DON'T KNOW, IT SEEMS TO BE AT ME!

HEE-
HEE!

WHEN I STARTED DOING THAT I WAS MORE DISCREET, WASN'T I?

"THE SPACEMEN CAME IN THEIR SAUCER!"

"AND WERE ABOUT TO REACH THE PLANET THEY LONGED TO SEE!"

CRASH!

"AND THEY WERE LUCKY ENOUGH TO AVOID DISAPPOINTMENT"

ALL THIS TALK ABOUT THE "BURNT-OUT GENERATION"...

...DOESN'T INCLUDE US, DOES IT?

NO, WE ARRIVED LATER

SO HOW LONG D'YOU THINK IT'LL BE BEFORE WE START GETTING SINGED?

THE GOOD THING ABOUT A NEW YEAR IS THAT IT COMES FULL OF UNUSED DAYS

IT'S LIKE STARTING TO WRITE ON A FRESH BLOCK OF PAPER WITH LOVELY WHITE CLEAN PAGES

THE SHAME IS THAT SO MANY WILL SPILL THEIR DRINK OVER THE REST

LAST NIGHT I ASKED MY FATHER TO EXPLAIN SOME DIVISIONS
OH, THE WORK SET BY TEACHER, YES?

WRONG, MAFALDA, YOU SHOULD HAVE ASKED ME TO EXPLAIN

NO, THOSE BETWEEN RUSSIA AND CHINA, ARABS AND ISRAELIS, BLACKS AND WHITES, AND...

CIGAR'S
AMERICAN STYLE TOBACCO

IS IT JUST ME OR IS THERE REALLY A FAD ABOUT ANGLICIZING WORDS?

Don Manolo, the first class grocer, not just beans

but Bean's

CLICK!

SMOKE "MONSTER'S 81
GO ON!

...THE KING SIZE NATIONAL SPECIAL...
WITH SPANISH LANGUAGE SMOKE?

...AND COMPLETE FILTER
AH...

Milis Phorris
20 FILTER TIP CIGARETTES
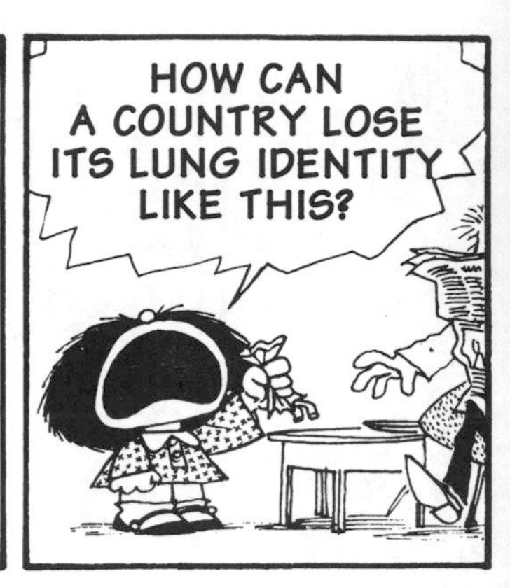
HOW CAN A COUNTRY LOSE ITS LUNG IDENTITY LIKE THIS?

HULLO, GUILLE. HOW ARE YOU?

EETEE, EETEE! BRRZS-DA-DA-AJGO!

GOOOiG-APBOOO! BADABADZZS NUiiiGJJH!

BAPOOO...
MYUM...

POOR BOY...STILL NOT IN CONTROL OF HIS PUBLIC RELATIONS!

BLONG!

HERE, BUT DON'T THROW IT AGAIN

BLONG!

DON'T START WASTING REBELLION, EH? ...YOU'RE GOING TO NEED IT LATER FOR LESS STUPID CAUSES

BOOM!
BANG!
RATAT-TAT-TAT-TAT-TAT!

BAM!
BOOM!

BOING!
BANG!
VIETNAM

WOULD YOU STOP THAT NOISE AND LET HUMANITY SLEEP IN PEACE?!!
VC

WE'RE SICK OF ALL THIS WAR THING...! SICK OF IT!
V.C.

SO GO AND TELL YOUR PRESIDENTS TO STOP BOTHERING US AND SIGN THE PEACE ONCE AND FOR ALL!

AND IF YOU DON'T HAVE A PEN I CAN LEND YOU MINE!

?

EXCUSE ME, SIR. ARE YOU NORTH AMERICAN?
NO, I DON'T HAVE ANY NATIONALITY

SO WHY THE STATUE OF LIBERTY?
I SELL IT, DEAR, I SELL IT

OF COURSE, IT'S NOT GENUINE. THAT WOULDN'T BE BUSINESS

BUT THE STATUE OF LIBERTY YOU SELL HAS NO FLAME

'CAUSE YOU CAN LIGHT IT PRESSING HERE. SEE?
CLICK

YEAH, I SEE

PAPA, WHAT'S ALL THAT ABOUT THE *PEOPLES' RIGHT TO SELF DETERMINATION?*

IT IS THE RIGHT OF EACH COUNTRY TO GOVERN ITSELF AS IT SEES BEST

THOSE WERE THE DAYS!
?

REMEMBER WHEN YOU TOLD ME THE STORIES AT BEDTIME?

MY FATHER SAYS THAT EACH COUNTRY HAS THE RIGHT TO GOVERN ITSELF AS IT SEES BEST

MAFALDA'S FATHER SAYS THAT EACH COUNTRY HAS THE RIGHT TO GOVERN ITSELF AS IT WISHES

HE SAYS THAT?
"DON MANOLO"
HE DOES

PAPA, IS IT TRUE THAT...?

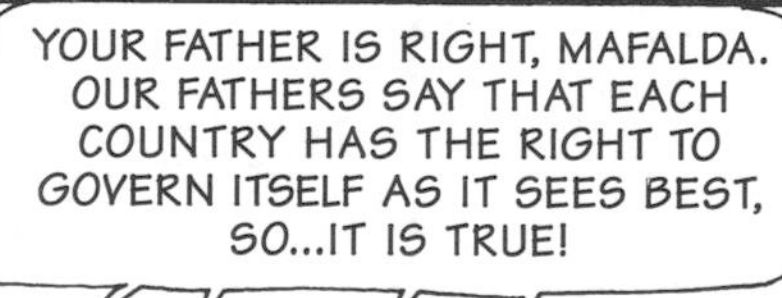
YOUR FATHER IS RIGHT, MAFALDA. OUR FATHERS SAY THAT EACH COUNTRY HAS THE RIGHT TO GOVERN ITSELF AS IT SEES BEST, SO...IT IS TRUE!

JUST LOOK AT HOW WE COME TO FIND THAT NEWS AGENCIES USE THE SCRIPT OF A CHEATING SADIST

...AND THAT WAS THE WORLD NEWS

LIES! ALL LIES. IT'S JUST NOT TRUE THAT THIS COUNTRY CONTROLS THAT ONE, OR THAT NATION IMPOSES ANYTHING BY FORCE ON ANOTHER! LIES!
CLICK!

'CAUSE MY DAD SAID EACH COUNTRY HAS THE RIGHT TO GOVERN ITSELF AS IT WISHES! AND THE TEACHER SAID RIGHTS MUST BE RESPECTED!

AND NEITHER MY FATHER NOR MY TEACHER WOULD SLEEP IN PEACE KNOWING THAT THEY SPEAK OF THINGS THAT DON'T WORK

WHAT'S UP? WHAT'RE YOU DRINKING?
OH? ER! NNNOTHING, JUST WATER
NERVECALM

OH, SO YOU'VE GOT PASTILLES, SUSANITA?
MYUP

OH...WELL, MEDICINE...YOU KNOW? THE DOCTOR GAVE THEM TO ME FOR SOMETHING OR OTHER

LIKE SOMETHING FAILING IN THE SHARING GLANDS?

YOU LOOK SMART, MANOLITO! WHERE'RE YOU GOING?

TO ASK FOR A LOAN FOR MY FATHER'S STORE
AND YOU THINK YOU'LL GET IT?

OF COUR...

Federation.
Bank of America chairman returns to United States

COULD YOU COME ROUND TOMORROW?

OH, MAFALDA, THOSE COMICS I PROMISED FOR TODAY...
TOMORROW, OK?

HEY, MAN! YOU BETTER SEE A DENTIST!
I WAS THINKING OF GOING TOMORROW

IF IT WEREN'T FOR TOMORROW, THIS WOULD BE THE *MAÑANA* COUNTRY

WOW! CAN YOU IMAGINE ALL WE'RE GOING TO SEE OVER THE NEXT TWO HUNDRED YEARS?

I DOUBT WE'LL BE HERE IN TWO HUNDRED YEARS, MIGUELITO

GO ON, YOU'RE THINKING OF MISSING OUT ON THE FUTURE JUST WHEN IT GETS INTERESTING?

PEACE!

ALLEGORICAL, THE LADY

SOMETIMES IT'S NOT GOOD TO BE LITTLE, BUT THEN WE HAVE LIFE AHEAD OF US. D'YOU SEE? **EVERYTHING** AWAITS US!

WE STUDY, GRADUATE, WORK, MARRY, HAVE KIDS, PROGRESS

BECOME AN ADULT, HAVE GRANDCHILDREN... AND, THE REST!

NO!...NOT THE HOME!

OH, MAFALDA, ISN'T IT GREAT TO BE **HERE** ON WALL STREET AND WATCH SUCH REFINED AND ELEGANT MILLIONAIRES GO BY

YAH BOOH!

YOUR JEERING CHEQUES BOUNCE AT MY GOOD CHEER BANK

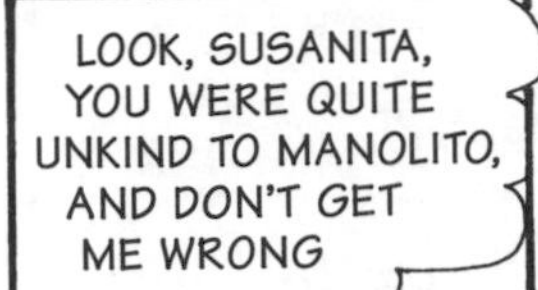
LOOK, SUSANITA, YOU WERE QUITE UNKIND TO MANOLITO, AND DON'T GET ME WRONG

OH, PLEASE!

HOW COULD I FEEL BAD ABOUT THAT WHEN IT COMES FROM THE LIPS OF A FRIEND LIKE YOU

I'D NEVER NOTICED...YOU HAVE AWFUL LIPS. POOR MAFALDA!

SWISH

SWISH

SWISH - - -

SWISH

WE DON'T WANT TO START SPRING WITH BAD NEWS

ISN'T SPRING LOVELY? THE TREES HAVE THEIR EARLY LEAVES

THE PARK IS FULL OF FLOWERS AND BUTTERFLIES

THE BIRDS SING WITH CHEER IN THEIR NESTS, THE AIR IS WARMER, THE DAYS'RE LONGER

THE NIGHTS SHORTER, PEOPLE CHANGE THEIR WINTER CLOTHES FOR LIGHTER MORE COLOURED ITEMS

AND WHO WILL REMOVE THIS AWFUL SCHOOL ALIENATION?!

THERE WAS A YOUNG WOMAN ON A PARK BENCH

AND EACH MAN PASSING LOOOOOKED AT HER
LIKE THAT

I DIDN'T UNDERSTAND WHY, SO I SAT OPPOSITE AND SPENT HALF AN HOUR LOOKING AT HER TO SEE WHAT IT WAS SHE HAD
AND?

IT MUST BE SOMETHING I DON'T KNOW ABOUT, BECAUSE I GOT VERY BORED

Z Z Z
Z Z

Z
Z Z
Z Z
©QUINO

ISN'T HE BECOMING
TOO BOURGEOIS?

LET'S PLAY LADIES LIKE YOUR
MOTHER AND MY MOTHER?
YES! AND...

WE GET TOGETHER FOR
TEA AND CHAT LIKE
LADIES

GOOD...
LET'S SEE...

WHO MAKES
THE FIRST STUPID
REMARK?

OH DEAR! WE HAVE CHATTED! DELICIOUS TEA, MRS MAFALDA!
THANK YOU, MRS SUSANITA

TELL ME, HAVE YOU ANY NEWS ABOUT FASHIONS THIS SEASON?
WELL, I HAVE READ THAT...

...INJUSTICE IS BEING WORN A LOT, NATURALLY WITH SOME VERY ELEGANT GROTESQUE

I DON'T SEE WHY SOME PEOPLE TRY TO PLAY LADIES IF THEY CAN'T KEEP UP STANDARDS

SURPRISING! MY THUMB IS LARGER THAN THE TOWER ON THAT HOUSE!

DO YOU KNOW WHY YOU SEE IT LARGER, MIGUELITO?
OF COURSE

BECAUSE THE THUMB IS **MINE** AND IS MORE IMPORTANT THAN THE TOWER

SLURP! GLUG! SLURP!

HAVE YOU FINISHED YOUR SOUP, MAFALDA?
YUCK! YES!

OH, YOU MEAN THE SOUP IN THE PLATE, NOT WHAT'S LEFT ON YOUR FACE! WIPE YOUR MOUTH!
DON'T WORRY

IT'LL BE WORSE WHEN A PSYCHOANALYST HAS TO CLEAN THE LEFTOVERS ON MY SUBCONSCIOUS

LOOK, GUILLE, A BOY LIKE YOU

SAME GENERATION, SEE?

GRAAAH!

Rip
Rip
Rip
CHIRP
RIP
RIP
Rip

BETTER NOT DRAW CONCLUSIONS

YOU KNOW I THINK ABOUT IT, BUT IT'S NO USE! HOW DOES TIME TURN THE CORNERS ON A SQUARE CLOCK?

MAMA, DO YOU THINK THAT COMMUNIST CHIN
I THINK YOU SHOULD WORRY ABOUT THINGS RIGHT FOR A GIRL YOUR AGE! I THINK!
SOAP

SOAP

YIPPEEE! LOVELY!

THAT'S IT
DO YOU THINK THAT COMMUNIST CH

YOUR MA'S RIGHT. YOU SHOULD DO THINGS YOUR AGE! LET'S GO BOWLING OR PLAY SOMETHING?
NAAH. NOT THE GAMES...

RACK!

TRACK! TRACK! TRACK!

©QUINO

TROC! TROC! TROC!

THESE ARE MORE STUPID, BUT THEY HAVE THE SIMPLICITY OF THE CLASSICS

LET ME SHOW YOU MY SWORD

ISN'T IT GREA...?

IT'S THE NAIL THAT'S NO GOOD

IT SHOULD BE ONE OF THOSE WITH TURNS AND A THREAD IN THE MIDDLE, KNOW WHAT I MEAN?

HELLO, FELIPE, WHAT'S UP?
NOTHING, JUST THAT I DIDN'T DO MY SCHOOLWORK BECAUSE I WAS READING COMICS

AND I DID NOT ENJOY THE COMICS BECAUSE I KNEW THAT I HAD WORK TO DO

NOW I AM DISTRESSED BECAUSE I HAVE STILL NOT DONE MY SCHOOLWORK
SO WHY DON'T YOU JUST GO AND DO IT?

I WILL, I WILL, BUT IF I DID NOT ENJOY THE COMICS AT LEAST LET ME ENJOY MY ANXIETY

WHEN IT'S NOT HIS SCHOOLWORK IT'S SOMETHING ELSE. FELIPE IS ALWAYS FINDING SOME WAY TO FEEL UPSET

I SAY THAT OF FELIPE, BUT I THINK WE ALL ARE A BIT LIKE HIM

BECAUSE IF WE HAD TO PASS AN EXAM TO KNOW HOW TO MANAGE OURSELVES...

I'D LIKE TO KNOW WHO'S THE BIG GUY THAT HAS THE LICENCE

WHAT'S UP WITH THE FACE? COME ON, LET'S GO AND GOSSIP

LAST NIGHT MY MOTHER TALKED ABOUT ALL SHE'D SPENT AT THE SUPERMARKET

SO MY FATHER SAID, "THAT'S TERRIBLE" AND THAT HE HAD A BAD DAY AT THE OFFICE AND A HEADACHE

MY MOTHER TOLD HIM, YOU'VE ALWAYS GOT A HEADACHE WHEN I SPEAK

GREETINGS, YOU TWO ORIGINALS

HE'S HAVING A BAD TIME...

DOESN'T EVEN HAVE A PLACE WHERE HE CAN DROP

HE'S BADLY INFORMED. THE WORLD TODAY OFFERS A GREAT VARIETY OF PLACES FOR THAT

NO, YOU'RE GETTING ME HOOKED ON YOUR BAD NEWS

I AM CONVINCED THE WORLD WILL BE FINE
WHEN?

THE DAY THE BAD MANAGERS VANISH

DON'T BE SO SURE, FELIPE. THAT SAME DAY SOMEBODY WILL COME ALONG AND PICK UP THE TORCH OF HORROR

HA-HA HA-HA

WHAT'S ALL THAT ABOUT, MANOLITO?
I GOT A BAD MARK IN GEOMETRY TODAY

AND IF YOU DON'T FACE THE BAD MOMENTS WITH A SMILE, YOU'RE DEAD

HA-HA-HA HA-HA

NOT MUCH HOPE OF ESCAPING ALIVE

I'LL ASK HIM! I JUST HAVE TO GO UP TO HIM AND ASK, WHATEVER HAPPENS!

EXCUSE ME, SIR. IS IT TRUE, WHAT MY MOTHER SAYS, THAT IF I... IF I DON'T... YOU KNOW, ABOUT DIRTY HANDS AND WASHING BEFORE LUNCH AND ALL THAT... YOU'LL PUT ME UNDER... WELL, YOU KNOW?

GO TELL YOUR MOTHER THAT POLICE HAVE BETTER THINGS TO DO!

I BEGIN TO UNDERSTAND ABOUT RESPECT FOR THE INSTITUTIONS
?

CAN YOU IMAGINE A WOMAN PRESIDENT, FELIPE?
GOD HELP US!

YOU BETTER LEARN THAT WOMEN ARE MORE INTELLIGENT THAN MEN! D'YOU HEAR ME?

AND NICER AND MORE NOBLE! GET IT?

SWEETER AND GENTLER! UNDERSTAND?

AND THEY SAY WOMEN ARE HARD TO UNDERSTAND!

I'M SICK OF BOYS WHO THINK WOMEN ARE *INFERIOR*
PROBABLY BECAUSE THEY SEE US IN HOUSE-WORK

WELL, THAT'S WHAT WOMEN ARE FOR! AFTER ALL, A WOMAN THAT DOESN'T COOK, IRON, WASH, CLEAN AND ALL THAT, IS **LESS** WOMAN, REALLY!

OH, SO A WOMAN WHO EMPLOYS A COOK, CLEANER, MAID AND THAT, IS LESS WOMAN?

HOLD IT! ONE THING'S BEING A WOMAN, STATUS IS QUITE ANOTHER

THE TROUBLE IS THAT WOMAN HAS HAD NO ROLE, BUT HAS PLAYED A **RAG** IN THE HISTORY OF HUMANITY

HERE, I THOUGHT I'D KEEP THE CHANGE TO BUY CHOCOLATE, BUT I COULDN'T

ALL BECAUSE THAT HORRIBLE TENANT SAID, *THIS IS ALL WRONG*, THAT *IS NOT DONE*, AND ALL THAT!

TENANT? WHAT TENANT?

THE ONE I'VE GOT INSIDE

DON'T YOU FEEL AS IF YOU HAD A TENANT INSIDE THAT SAYS THINGS?
OF COURSE

IT'S NO TENANT, BUT THE VOICE OF CONSCIENCE WHICH SAYS THINGS TO US, LIKE YOU

LIKE ME, YES! BUT JUST THINK IF A CONSCIENCE CAN TREAT A GENERAL ON FIRST NAME BASIS

GROCERIES "DON MANOLO"
MANOLITO, DOES YOUR CONSCIENCE SPEAK TO YOU OFTEN?

ER, YES...THE OTHER DAY IT WAS ON ABOUT HEALTH THIS, AND HEALTH THAT...

BUT LUCKY I IGNORED IT, BECAUSE PEOPLE BOUGHT ALL THOSE CANS ANYWAY

HAVE YOU HEARD OF THE VOICE OF CONSCIENCE, MIGUELITO?
YES

HOW IS YOUR
HOARSE!

IT'S CERTAIN THE RANKING OF FAILURES DOES NOT START WITH PEOPLE LIKE HIM

AND HOW DOES ONE STICK THIS ON THE SOUL?

IT ALSO BREAKS MY HEART TO SEE POOR PEOPLE, BELIEVE ME!

THAT'S WHY WHEN WE BECOME LADIES WE WILL JOIN A FOUNDATION TO HELP THE NEEDY

AND WE'LL HOLD BANQUETS AND SERVE TURKEY, AND CHICKEN AND ROAST MEATS AND THAT... AND WE'LL RAISE MONEY

TO BUY FLOUR AND GRAIN AND DRY BISCUITS AND THOSE HORRIBLE THINGS THE POOR EAT

MY GRANDDAD KEEPS SAYING THAT IN HIS DAYS THINGS WERE BETTER THAN NOW

AND THAT PEOPLE WERE KINDER AND HAPPIER
BEST IGNORE HIM, MIGUELITO

YEH, I KNOW! HE SAYS IT SO OFTEN, WHO'S GOING TO TAKE ANY NOTICE?
OF COURSE

MY GRANDDAD KEEPS SAYING THAT IN HIS DAYS THINGS WERE BETTER THAN NOW AND PEOPLE WERE KIND

TELL ME, PAPA, WERE THINGS BETTER THAN NOW IN YOUR DAYS?

WELL...THERE WERE FEWER NUCLEAR WEAPONS, LESS SUBVERSION, FEWER RACE RIOTS... WHAT CAN I SAY?

I WANTED YOU TO SAY THAT THESE ARE YOUR DAYS, BUT I SEE YOU ARE HALF FINISHED!

?

DID I TELL YOU MY LITTLE BROTHER CAN CRAWL, FELIPE?

I TOLD MAMA IT'S AWFUL THAT SHE LOCKED YOU UP LIKE THIS!

AND I TOLD HER IT WAS A BREACH OF INDIVIDUAL FREEDOMS AND THE DECLARATION OF HUMAN RIGHTS! YES, SIR!

BUT IT SEEMS THAT HAS NOTHING TO DO WITH EATING THE EARTH IN THE FLOWERPOTS, GUILLE

NO USE! HOWEVER MUCH THE TEACHER EXPLAINS, I DON'T UNDERSTAND THIS ABOUT THE SUBJECT AND PREDICATE!

EASY, MIGUELITO. IF I SAY, *"THE TRASH MAKES THE STREET LOOK UGLY"*, WHICH IS THE SUBJECT?

THE MAYOR?

MIGUELITO IS HAVING TROUBLE WITH THE SUBJECT AND PREDICATE
TROUBLE IS THEY COME UP WITH SUCH THINGS AT SCHOOL!

YESTERDAY THE TEACHER DECIDED TO TEST US ON MENTAL SPEED

"WHAT'S THIS?" ZOOOOOOM! "WHAT'S THAT?" ZOOOOM!
SO HOW DID YOU DO?

LIKE A PEDESTRIAN OF REASON

WELL?

OK, READY!

BY THE WAY, THE TOOTHPASTE WAS A LITTLE TEMPERAMENTAL TODAY. SO MIND YOU DON'T SLIP IN THE BATHROOM

I TRUST YOU TRUST HE TRUSTS

WE TRUST THEY TRUST

INGENUOUS, AREN'T THEY?!

WHEN I GROW UP I'LL BE A FILM AND TV STAR. IMAGINE. I'LL BE IN ALL THE MAGAZINES!

OF COURSE I'LL GET MARRIED AND DIVORCED, AND THEN MARRY AGAIN AND AGAIN DIVORCE. I DON'T LIKE THAT AT ALL...

BETTER TO HAVE ONE RELIABLE HUSBAND AND LOTS OF CHILDREN, AND BE A GOOD HOUSEWIFE, AND THAT'S IT

BACK FROM HER BREAKDOWN OVER THE SHARP RISE IN TOMATO PRICES, SUSANITA FACES THE FUTURE WITH COURAGE

OF COURSE, I'LL NEVER GET INTO THE MAGAZINES

I WONDER IF WHEN MY MOTHER WAS LITTLE SHE WANTED TO BE WHAT SHE IS NOW

MAMA!

WHAT D'YA WANT!?

JUST THINKING ABOUT A BOY WHO NEARLY PUT A FINGER IN THE FAN, BUT NEVER MIND

SO, WHAT IS THE HOMEWORK FOR TOMORROW?
LET ME SEE...

AN ESSAY ON *"THE WORLD OF THE FUTURE"*
AND SOME SENTENCES ON THE FUTURE OF THE VERB *TO LIVE*

SENTENCES OR PRAYERS?

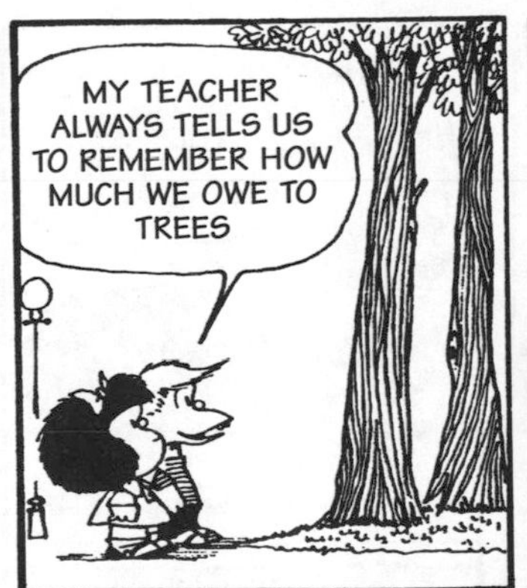
MY TEACHER ALWAYS TELLS US TO REMEMBER HOW MUCH WE OWE TO TREES

SHADE IN SUMMER, WOOD IN WINTER, WOOD FOR BUILDING HOMES, SHIPS, FURNITURE AND MUCH MORE

THAT'S WHY SHE SAYS WE MUST LOOK AFTER THE TREES

AND DIDN'T SHE SAY THERE IS ALWAYS A REVISIONIST?

WAAAH!

WAAAH!

W...!

SPLASH!
GAAA! YIP! YIP!
SPLASH! SPLASH!

SO, WE'VE JOINED THE REBEL CONFORMIST LINE? VERY PRETTY!

YOOOHOOO!
PAPA'S HOME, GUILLE

YEEE!

!?

LOOKS LIKE THE FAMILY CHIEF'S A SOFTY

RIGHT,
NOW WE'LL STUDY
THE PENTAGON

AND TOMORROW
THE KREMLIN?
TRAC!

FOR THE SAKE
OF BALANCE

TOYS
GAMES

TOYS
GAMES

YOU'VE GOT SOME
GOOD NEWS YOU DON'T WANT
TO TELL US!

CAN YOU BELIEVE IT!
THE CHEEKY THING WAS MARRIED IN WHITE! I ASK YOU?!

WHY ASK? ISN'T THAT DONE EVERYWHERE?

OR ARE WE FACING A CHEEKINESS BOOM?!

MAMA, WHY DO BRIDES WEAR WHITE WHEN THERE ARE SO MANY OTHER COLOURS?

BECAUSE WHITE IS CLEAN AND PURE. A BRIDE WHO DOESN'T WEAR WHITE IS... I DON'T KNOW...

A BRIDE WITH A LITTLE DIRT?

DID YOU SEE THAT NEW GAME ON TV?
WHICH?

THE ONE THAT SAYS...
KIDS! HAPPINESS FOR ALL IS HERE!

AH, YES!

YEAH! JUST LOOK AT THE HAPPINESS THEY SELL YOU ON TV

WHO'D HAVE THOUGHT THIS GAME WAS STUPID? IT LOOKED SO GOOD ON TV!
AS THE SAYING HAS IT, FELIPE

"NOT ALL THAT SHINES IS GOLD"

1034

ALL WE NEED NOW IS FOR THE SUN TO BE CALLED CHEAP GOODS!

DON'T YOU THINK MANY PEOPLE BUY TRASH JUST BECAUSE THEY SEE IT SOLD ON TELEVISION?

YES, SOMETIMES TV ADVERTS SELL STUFF AS GOOD BUT... OH WELL!

I CAN'T BEAR TO SEE THAT! I CAN'T BEAR TO SEE PEOPLE BEING CHEATED!

HELLO, MANOLITO, GIVE ME 1/2 A KILO OF DRY FRUIT, THE GOOD ONES, EH?
OF COURSE

YOU'VE GOT TO COVER YOUR EYES, MAFALDA

1036

ABBAA! DABOOO! DAB!

SO YOUNG AND WHEN WATCHING TV HE REASONS JUST LIKE ANY GROWN-UP!

ALL FOR THE HOME
BOOKS
WORLD NEWS

ALL FOR THE HOME

ALL FOR THE HOME

ALL FOR THE HOME

ALL FOR THE HOME
?
FOR SALE
-WITH TENANTS-
5 CONTINENTS
2 POLES AND STORE SPACE
VANDALS NEED NOT APPLY

I NEVER THOUGHT I COULD! NEVER!

NEVER DID I THINK I COULD DO SOMETHING AS AWFUL AS THIS TO SOMEBODY, FELIPE! I SWEAR
© QUINO

YOU CAN'T EVEN TRUST YOURSELF! WHAT A STATE, I SAY! WHAT A STATE!

OH, OH!

LISTEN TO THIS ARTICLE, MANOLITO: "ACCORDING TO THE PAKISTANI PHYSICIST ABDUS SALAM, IN TWENTY YEARS...

...THE DEVELOPING WORLD WILL BE AS POOR AND AS HUNGRY AS NOW"

MANOLITO IS INFURIATING!
AAAAAH!...
SEE WHAT A BRUTE HE IS? I ALWAYS SAY HE'S A BRUTE!

I READ HIM AN ARTICLE WHERE A PHYSICIST SAYS THAT IN TWENTY YEARS THERE WILL BE HUNGER LIKE NOW...

...AND HE IS DELIGHTED THAT WE WON'T SEE SOCIAL CHANGE! YOU HAVE TO BE A REAL BEAST TO THINK AS HE DOES!

DON'T YOU DARE INSULT ME!

TROOPS

BIG BATTLES OUTSIDE THE

THINGS MUST GET BETTER, PAPA. DON'T WORRY YOUR BROW

SOME THINGS THE POOR MAN JUST CAN'T DO ON HIS OWN

NO LEFT TURN

NO BILL POSTING

NO PARKING

IT'S COMFORTING TO SEE HOW MAN HAS GRADUALLY REMOVED THE LIMITS TO HIS FREEDOM TO LIMIT HIMSELF

WHAT A HABIT! ALL THEY DO IS FORBID THINGS!

MIGUELITO, DON'T YOU FIND THIS NOTICE OFFENSIVE?

KEEP OFF THE GRASS

NO. WHO CARES? I HAVE MY OWN LITTLE INTERIOR LAWN

MAFALDA, WASH YOUR HANDS AND COME'N EAT

HAVE YOU WASHED?

YES! IT'S THE SAME THING EVERY DAY

"WASH YOUR HANDS FOR LUNCH"

"WASH YOUR HANDS FOR SUPPER"

WHAT A PILATE OBSESSION, EH?

GOOD DAY, DARLING. IS YOUR PAPA HOME?
DEPENDS, WHAT FOR?

TO OFFER HIM THE NEW SUPER "NOBALDY" TONIC, THE ONLY BRAND THAT AVOIDS AND BEATS BALDING
TONICO

HEAD BALDNESS, OR IDEAS BALDNESS

WHO WAS IT?
SOMEBODY UNIMPORTANT

SHARE? HAH!
OK

THE DEVIL WILL COME AND PUNISH YOU FOR BEING SELFISH AND HORRID! YOU'LL SEE!
SLURP! SLURP!

CROCK! CRUNCH!

SCHUIIP! SCHUIIP!

HE MUST HAVE MISSED THE BUS

I ASSURE YOU THAT SEEING THAT WOULD SHRINK ANYBODY'S HEART!
1048

I DOUBT IT. MOST OF THE WORLD WEARS IT PRESHRUNK

WALK INTO ANY TOY SHOP AND WHAT D'YOU SEE? WEAPONS, WAR TOYS...! HUGE VARIETIES OF TOY GUNS!

THIS IS NOT NEW! GENERATIONS AND GENERATIONS HAVE GROWN UP UNDER THE INFLUENCE OF THESE HORRIBLE TOYS...

...THAT ENCOURAGE VIOLENCE AND AGGRESSION, INCITE WAR! THAT IS WHY THE WORLD IS AS IT IS!

I KNEW IT! IT WASN'T OIL, OR MULTINATIONAL INTERESTS, NONE OF THOSE SIMPLE ISSUES ARE TO BLAME!

BANG!
BANG!
CRACK!
SLAM!

WHAT'S UP, MIGUELITO?
DIDN'T YOU SEE WHAT THEY SAID ON TV ABOUT TOY GUNS?

YES
WELL, I DON'T WANT TOYS THAT TEACH ME HOW TO KILL
BANG!
CRACK!
BANG!

I WANT TO BE SELF-TAUGHT!

SNIFF?
SNIFF?

1051

KNOW SOMETHING? GUILLE CAN STAND
YES?

WITHOUT HOLDING ON TO ANYTHING?

CLONK!

WAAH!
WILL YOU SHUT UP? SHUT UP I SAY!

OOOH! LOOK, THAT LITTLE GIRL IS LIKE YOU AND IS NOT CRYING! SHAME! SHE IS LOOKING AT YOU! SHE'LL THINK YOU'RE A CRYBABY, WON'T YOU, DEAR?

NO!

LUCKY THAT THE GIRL HAS A TRADE UNIONIST CONSCIENCE

"THERE IS NO EVIL THAT
LASTS 100 YEARS"

DON'T KNOW ABOUT A HUNDRED,
BUT THERE ARE A QUITE A FEW
GREY-HAIRED EVILS

"RIGHT, FRIENDS,
LET'S READ THIS STORY
AND LET FLY OUR IMAGINATION"

THOSE WITH NO CEILING,
OF COURSE

MAMA, WHAT WOULD YOU LIKE TO BE IF YOU HAD A LIFE?

DO YOU THINK THAT CLEANING THE HOUSE ALL DAY IS LIFE, SUSANITA?

WHY NOT? MY GRANDMOTHER HAS DONE NOTHING ELSE AND IS 83. WHAT D'YOU SAY TO THAT?

IF LIFE IS LASTING, I PREFER ONE BEATLES SONG TO A "BOSTON POPS" ALBUM

SEE? WITHOUT ME YOU ARE NOTHING

WHAT WILL THE MOON LOOK LIKE WHEN MAN HAS BUILT CITIES THERE, FULL OF WIDE STREETS, HIGH BUILDINGS AND GLITTERING SIGNS?

DAMAGED, I SUPPOSE

THE GOVERNMENT DOES LISTEN TO THE ARGUMENTS OF CRITICS OF THE LAW...

BUT WARNS THAT NO GROUP INTEREST WILL PREVENT ITS INTRODUCTION WITH FULL FORCE

YOU LET 'EM HAVE IT!

I'M GOING TO READ YOUR FUTURE, FELIPE. TAKE A CARD

NOW TURN AROUND, RUB IT ON YOUR NOSE AND SAY, "TRUE, TRUE. I GIVE YOU MY FUTURE"

"TRUE, TRUE. I GIVE YOU MY FUTURE"

NOW GIVE IT TO ME AND SAY, "UKA-UKA"
"UKA-UKA"

RIGHT, I SEE YOUR FUTURE AS A SIMPLETON READY TO DO ANY STUPIDITY YOU'RE ASKED FOR

PSSST! MAFALDA, CHOOSE A CARD AND KNOW YOUR FUTURE

NONSENSE, THE UN WROTE ITS OWN YEARS AGO AND LOOK WHAT HAPPENED

MAMA SAYS DON'T SEND THE DELIVERY, MANOLITO, BECAUSE NEXT WEEK WE'RE ON VACATION
I UNDERSTAND

HAH!

A FEW YEARS AGO ANYBODY WEARING THIS WOULD SEEM MAD TO ME
GO ON!

YOU DON'T REALLY MEAN YOU WERE THAT GOOD AT TELLING THE FUTURE

AAAH! AT LAST WE'RE HERE!

SAME PROBLEM!

WHEN YOU LOOK AT PEOPLE ON HOLIDAY...

...THEY LOOK AS IF THEY WEREN'T GUILTY OF ANYTHING

AND THIRDLY, YOU WERE WRONG TO LEAVE...

...AND IN TWELFTH PLACE...

HULLO, WHAT'S YOUR NAME?

MARIA ALEXANDRA DEL PILAR UGARTE LACLOS

YOU POOR THING! JUST THINK HOW MUCH TIME YOU WOULD SAVE TO DO OTHER THINGS WITH A SHORTER NAME!

!

WOW! IT FELT LIKE AN URGENT NEWS REPORT!

HEY! WHAT?!

NOTHING! JUST THAT YOU HAD A BIKINI IN YOUR EYE

WHEN YOU COMPARE PLANET EARTH WITH THE UNIVERSE IT IS AS SMALL AS THIS GRAIN OF SAND

AND WE HUMAN BEINGS ARE JUST MICROBES, DON'T YOU THINK?

NO!

LISTEN, GUILLE. WHAT DO YOU HEAR?

TOOT-TOOT-TOOT-TOOT-TOOT-TOOT...

OOOH!
ONE COMES BACK FEELING SOMEBODY ELSE!

OH, AND THESE SILLY PEOPLE HAVE BEEN SENDING THE BILLS TO THE MAN YOU WERE BEFORE!

TELL ME ABOUT THE SEASIDE, MAFALDA. DID YOUR MOTHER FALL IN LOVE WITH THE LIFEGUARD?
LIFEGUARD?

YEAH, STUPID! LIFEGUARDS ARE BEAUTIFUL AND YOU DIDN'T NOTICE!

YES, I DID, BUT DIDN'T THINK OF HIM AS BEAUTIFUL. WHAT I THOUGHT WAS THAT WHILE HE GUARDED A FEW LIVES THOUSANDS OF BOMBS WERE BEING MADE AND...

SUSANITA?

YUP! MY FATHER THINKS THERE IS NO BETTER HOLIDAY THAN WORK

OF COURSE! HOLIDAYS MEAN SPENDING, WORK MEANS EARNING MONEY

MONEY!
AND HEALTH? ONE THING'S MONEY, HEALTH QUITE ANOTHER!

WHAT??!

I DIDN'T READ ANY NEWSMAGAZINES WHILE ON HOLIDAY, SO I'M GETTING UP TO DATE

AND I FOUND A SENTENCE, FELIPE... WHAT A SENTENCE
WHAT SENTENCE?

"BETTER DIE STANDING THAN LIVE ON YOUR KNEES"

I ASK YOU...IS IT DISHONOURABLE TO SURVIVE SEATED?

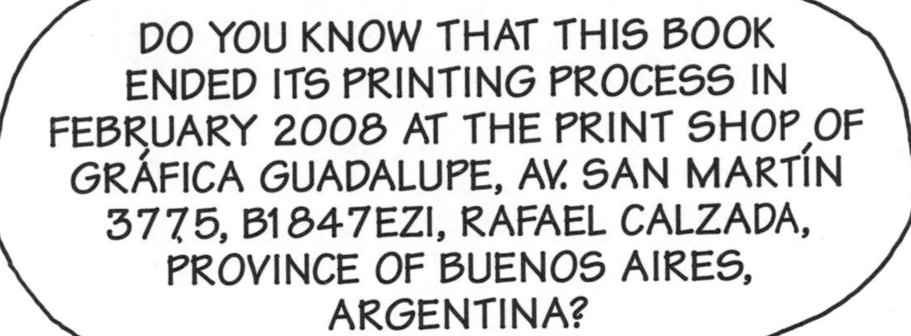
DO YOU KNOW THAT THIS BOOK ENDED ITS PRINTING PROCESS IN FEBRUARY 2008 AT THE PRINT SHOP OF GRÁFICA GUADALUPE, AV. SAN MARTÍN 3775, B1847EZI, RAFAEL CALZADA, PROVINCE OF BUENOS AIRES, ARGENTINA?

NOW YOU KNOW WHICH PRINT SHOP TO CONGRATULATE OR NOT, DEPENDING HOW THE PRINTING HAS IMPRESSED YOU

Edición de 3000 ejenplares.